MARVEL

ORIGIN STORIES

MARVEL

New York • Los Angeles

"Spider-Man" adapted by Rich Thomas Jr. Illustrated by The Storybook Art Group.
Based upon the Marvel comic book series *Spider-Man*.

"Iron Man" adapted by Rich Thomas Jr. Illustrated by Tom Grummett and Hi-Fi Design.
Based upon the Marvel comic book series *Iron Man*.

"X-Men" adapted by Rich Thomas Jr. Illustrated by The Storybook Art Group.
Based upon the Marvel comic book series *The X-Men*.

"The Avengers" adapted by Rich Thomas Jr. Illustrated by Pat Olliffe and Hi-Fi Design.
Based upon the Marvel comic book series *The Avengers*.

"Ant-Man" adapted by Scott Peterson. Illustrated by Rick Burchett and Hi-Fi Design.
Based upon the Marvel comic book series *The Avengers*.

"Wolverine" adapted by Alison Lowenstein. Illustrated by Val Semeiks and Hi-Fi Design.
Based upon the Marvel comic book series *The X-Men*.

"Wasp" adapted by Scott Peterson. Illustrated by Rick Burchett and Hi-Fi Design.
Based upon the Marvel comic book series *The Avengers*.

"Captain America Joins the Avengers" adapted by Rich Thomas Jr. Illustrated by Pat Olliffe and Hi-Fi Design.
Based upon the Marvel comic book series *The Avengers*.

"All-New X-Men" adapted by Rich Thomas. Illustrated by Pat Olliffe and The Storybook Art Group.
Based upon the Marvel comic book series *The X-Men*.

"The Fantastic Four" adapted by Alison Lowenstein. Illustrated by Pat Olliffe and Hi-Fi Design.
Based upon the Marvel comic book series *The Fantastic Four*.

"Daredevil" adapted by Scott Peterson. Illustrated by Pat Olliffe and Hi-Fi Design.
Based upon the Marvel comic book series *Daredevil*.

Printed in China
First Edition
1 3 5 7 9 10 8 6 4 2
ISBN 978-1-4231-9964-9
F383-2370-2-13214

TABLE OF CONTENTS

Peter Parker was a student at Midtown High. Peter enjoyed all his classes, but science was his favorite. He was the best student Midtown High had seen in many years. His teachers were very proud of him, but the other students made fun of him.

One day, Peter heard about a great demonstration at the Science Hall. He asked the other kids if they wanted to join him.

The other students just laughed at Peter. One of them, a bully named **Flash Thompson**, even pushed him to the ground.

By the time Peter arrived at the Science Hall, he had forgotten all about his classmates' cruel actions. All he could think about was the experiment. He couldn't wait to see how the scientists would control a **radioactive wave**!

The rays were ready.

Peter eagerly looked on. But so did something else. The demonstration was about to begin!

Peter was thrilled to be there, in the company of such brilliant scientists. He wanted to be just like them—smart, talented . . . amazing!

Everyone was so fascinated by the demonstration that no one noticed when something unplanned occurred. A spider descended between the rays just as they were activated.

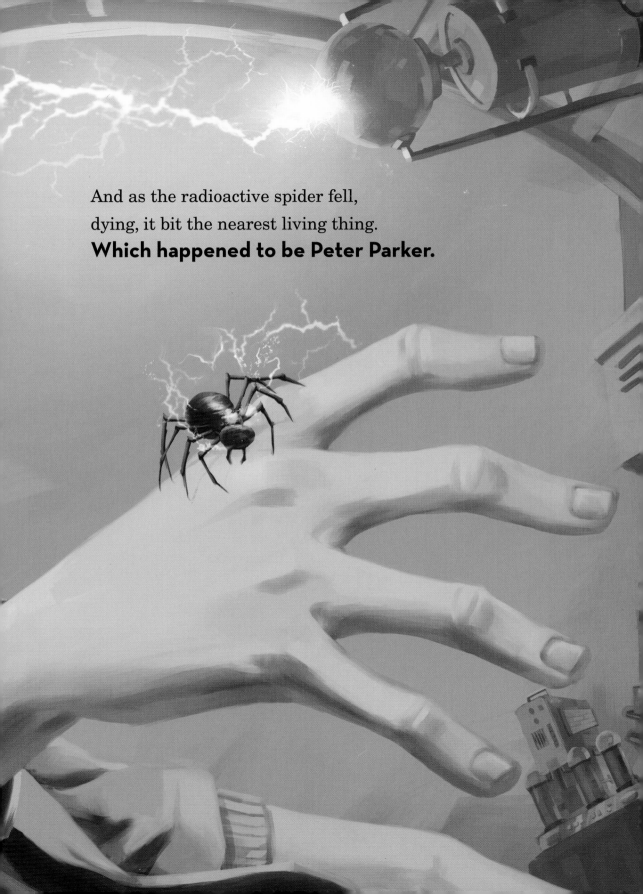

And as the radioactive spider fell,
dying, it bit the nearest living thing.
Which happened to be Peter Parker.

Peter started to feel weak and tired. The room began
to spin. The scientists noticed that Peter looked ill, and
they offered to help him.

But Peter just wanted to get out of the dark laboratory
and into the fresh air.

Peter felt a peculiar tingling in his head. It was an itching, urging, nagging feeling. The only thing he understood about it was that he was meant to react.

To do

something.

So he did.

Peter was sure he was dreaming.

He couldn't really be **climbing** up
a wall. Nobody could do that.

When he reached the roof,
he grabbed on to a chimney—
and **crushed** it! He didn't
have that kind of strength.

Peter felt the tingly feeling again.
This time it gave him the urge to
spring. And so he **jumped** from
one tall roof to another.

When he wanted to go back
down to the street, the same
strange feeling told him the
easiest way to get there was to
climb down a clothesline.

Peter stared at himself in amazement. How could this be happening?

Then, Peter realized he had started feeling different right after being bitten by that spider in the lab. Somehow the experiment must have affected the dying creature. **And when it bit Peter, it transferred its power to him!**

As he wandered home, amazed and half-dazed, a sign outside an old wrestling theater caught his eye. It would be the perfect way to test all of his newfound abilities.

Peter rushed home.

And then he rushed
right back.

Peter was ready to test his new powers on a brutish wrestler called **Crusher Hogan**. Peter wore a disguise so that no one would make fun of him if his plan didn't work.

He'd been teased and taunted enough. When Peter challenged him, Crusher Hogan laughed.

But Crusher soon found that he was **very wrong** to do so.

Peter was paid well for the victory. A man in the crowd even asked him if he'd want to be on TV.

At home, Peter's **Aunt May** and **Uncle Ben** gave him a gift. It was a special microscope. Uncle Ben reminded Peter that knowledge and science were power. "And," Uncle Ben told Peter, **"with great power comes great responsibility."**

Peter was too excited to settle down. He used his new microscope, his chemistry set, and his knowledge of science to create a very special **fluid**.

The new substance had the strength and stickiness of a spider's silk. Then he created devices that could spin the fluid into a web the same way a spider would. He called them his **web-shooters**.

Finally, he designed a sleek new costume. Now all he needed was a stage name. **He arrived at one as good as any other. . . .**

SPIDER-MAN!

Peter's TV appearances were a huge hit.

After all, who wouldn't be amazed by a Spider-Man climbing up walls and swinging from his own webs?

Soon everyone wanted a piece of Spider-Man. Peter was
starting to feel important, wanted . . . **and powerful**.

Peter got lost thinking about how wonderful his new life would be. He daydreamed about fame and celebrity. When a security guard called for help down the studio hall, Peter ignored him.

The crook that the guard was chasing raced into an elevator and escaped.

But Peter didn't care. He had great power. From now on, he only needed to look out for one person—himself.

It didn't take long for Peter to forget about the officer and the escaped criminal. In fact, by the time he got home they were the furthest things from his mind. He was just happy to be with the people who loved him.

One night on his way home from a TV performance, Peter arrived to find something worrisome.

Peter knew something was terribly wrong, and he was right. His Uncle Ben had been killed by a criminal. The police officers told Peter not to worry. They had the crook cornered at an old waterfront warehouse.

Peter ran upstairs,

put on his costume,

and swooped over the city to avenge his uncle.

Peter was **quicker and more furious** than ever before.

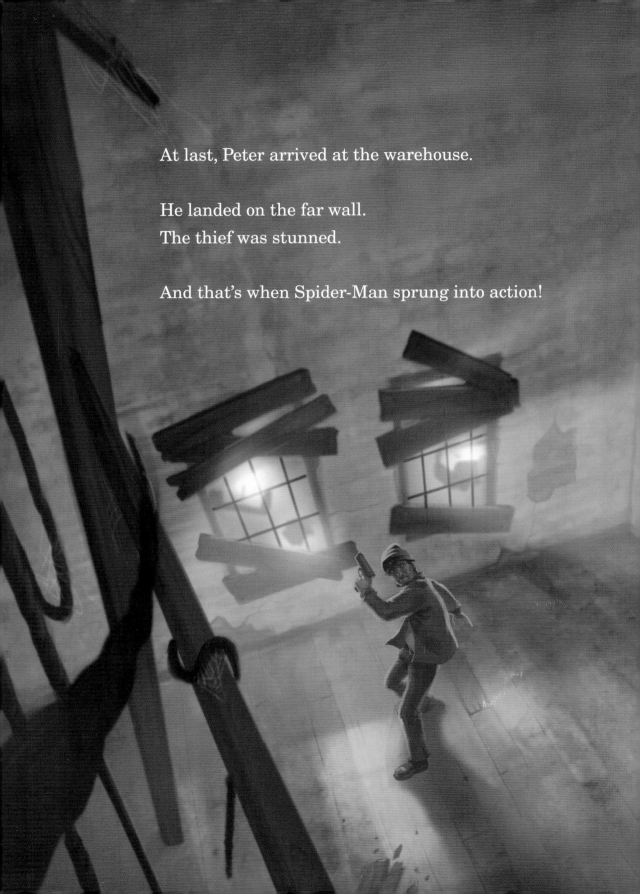

At last, Peter arrived at the warehouse.

He landed on the far wall.
The thief was stunned.

And that's when Spider-Man sprung into action!

The crook's hat flew from his head, and Peter got a good look at him. Peter felt a heavy weight in his chest. It couldn't be. But it was. The man who had killed his uncle was the same man he allowed to escape into the elevator at the studio.

If only Peter had stopped him then! If only he had not acted so selfishly!

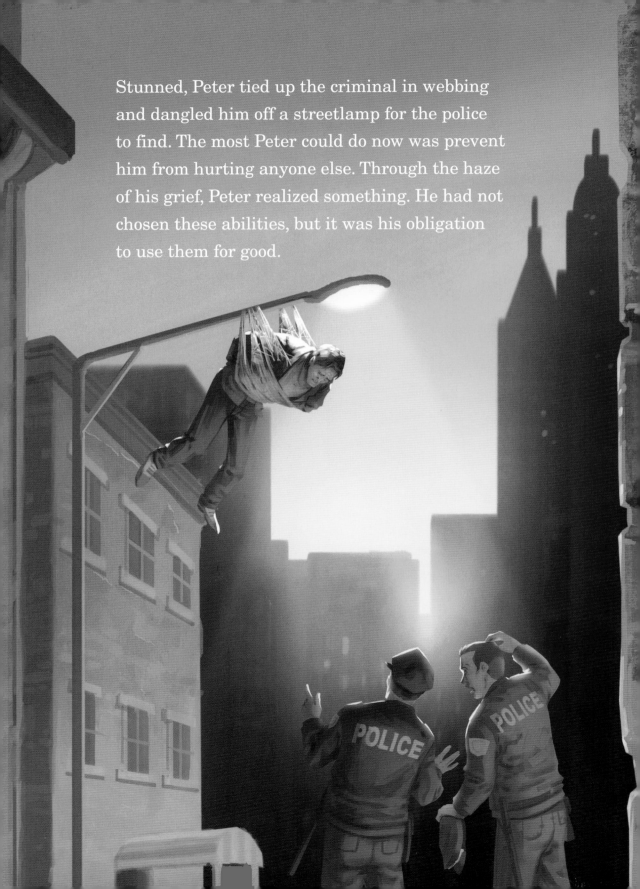

Stunned, Peter tied up the criminal in webbing and dangled him off a streetlamp for the police to find. The most Peter could do now was prevent him from hurting anyone else. Through the haze of his grief, Peter realized something. He had not chosen these abilities, but it was his obligation to use them for good.

It was not about money or fame or any of the other rewards his power could give him. He had finally realized that what his Uncle Ben had told him was true:

with great power comes great responsibility.

And that was the rule that Peter Parker
lived by from that day forward.

This is Tony Stark.

When Tony puts on his special armor, he becomes more powerful than most people. He even calls himself something different.

When he puts his armor on, Tony becomes . . .

THE INVINCIBLE IRON MAN!

But Tony wasn't born a Super Hero.

He hasn't always fought to protect people.

But Tony feels that it is his responsibility to stop villains such as **Titanium Man** and **Iron Monger**, who would use his technology for their own evil purposes.

Tony didn't always get the job done this easily.

Or this well.

Tony's armor wasn't always so sleek.

In fact, when he first became Iron Man, Tony's armor didn't even shine!

But if you really want to know how Iron Man was born, we need to start with the man behind the mask.

Tony Stark had so much money that he could go anywhere he wanted.

He loved to have fun.

And he loved the finer things in life.

But Tony also worked hard.
He was a brilliant inventor. He
knew all sorts of things about
science.

He loved to work with magnetic fields. Using them, he created a powerful energy force that he called repulsor technology.

The military was interested in Tony's work. In fact, it was in a **secret Army lab** that Tony's life was forever changed.

An enemy army attacked, and Tony was badly hurt!

Since Tony was famous, he was recognized right away.
The enemy knew all about his inventions.

The enemy tossed him in a prison room filled with electronic and mechanical equipment. They wanted him to create a mighty weapon for them.

To make things worse, the enemy told Tony that his heart had been hurt in the blast. **He did not have much longer to live.**

Tony soon found that he was not alone in the cell. The enemy had captured another famous scientist—**Professor Yinsen**. The enemy wanted the two men to work together on the great weapon.

But Professor Yinsen had other ideas—he knew a way to keep Tony alive!

The two men worked tirelessly to create
something that would save Tony's life . . .

Finally, the men completed the device. Tony would need to wear it on his chest from now on to keep his heart beating.

Using Tony's repulsors, they also built boots that could help a man **fly!**

Gloves that could **crush steel!**

And a helmet that could protect a man from the most **terrible blast!**

Tony put on the armor . . .

. . . and proved that no walls
could hold

the IRON MAN!

It wasn't long before the enemy realized that they were fighting a losing battle.

Having escaped from prison and saved
Professor Yinsen, Tony flew back home.

But almost as soon as he got there, he realized
that he could now help where others couldn't.

Tony to the rescue!

He was strong, unstoppable, **FRIGHTENING!**

Maybe a little **too frightening.**

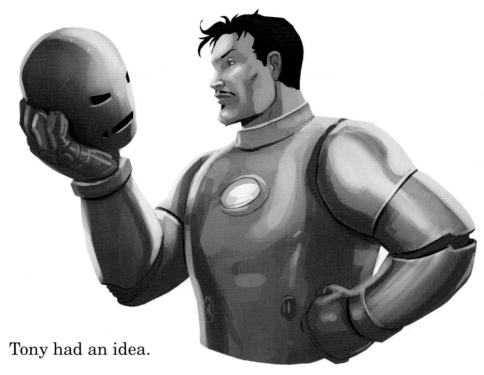

Tony had an idea.

Now his suit
was better.

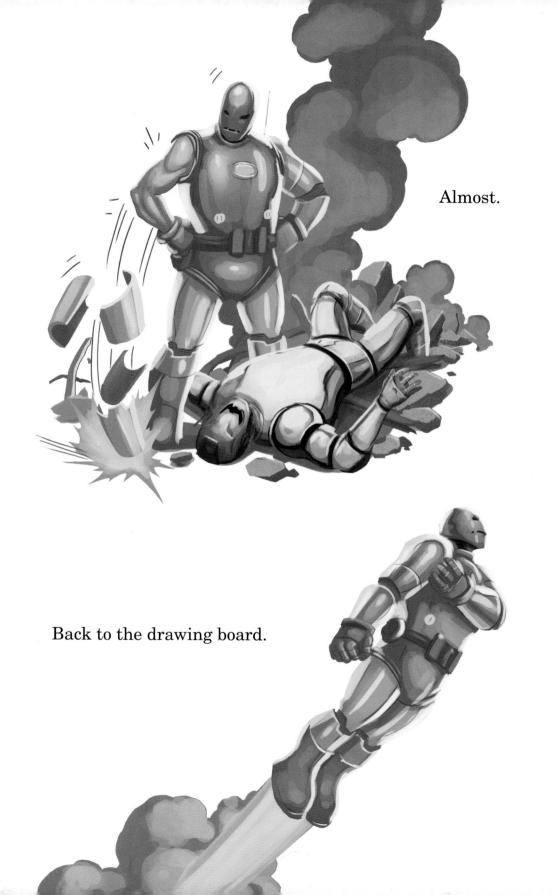

Almost.

Back to the drawing board.

Tony thought that Iron Man needed something as smooth and stylish as he was. He needed to create a lighter suit.

Soon, Tony perfected his armor. . . .

The **Invincible Iron Man** was born again!

And as Iron Man, Tony never stops fighting.

He protects people
at home . . .

. . . and around
the world.

And when he's not fighting for
justice as Iron Man . . .

. . . Tony runs his company, **Stark Industries**.

Stark Industries might need Tony to be a businessman.

But with new villains **attacking** every day,

the world needs Tony to be an

IRON MAN!

Did you ever have a dream that felt so real, you were sure you weren't **dreaming** at all?

This is a story about a boy named **Charles Xavier** who dreamed he could do many things that an ordinary boy could not.

He dreamed his mind could leave
his body and float like a feather.

He dreamed he could know what other
people were thinking before they even
opened their mouths to speak.

But Charles didn't want to tell other people about his special dreams, because he was afraid of how they would treat him.

So Charles dreamed of a world where people like himself—people who felt different—could be proud to be themselves.

The world didn't seem like a very fair place to Charles. His father had passed away when he was just a young boy.

Charles lived in his father's mansion with his mother, who loved him very much.

But his older brother and his stepfather lived in the
mansion, too. And they were heartless and cruel to
Charles and his mother.

Charles began to lose his hair at a very young age. And by the time he was a teenager, his head was completely bare.

But that was not all.

Charles had always heard whispers of things that no one was saying out loud. As he grew older, he began to hear them more and more clearly. Eventually, Charles realized that **he could read minds**.

As time went by and
Charles grew older, he
used his gift to gain
knowledge.

He studied to become a doctor of science. He wanted to
learn more about why he had these special powers.

Charles soon discovered that he was a **mutant**—a person born with special abilities.

Charles's studies took him all over the world. In Egypt, Charles met another mutant for the first time.

This mutant was **evil**. Charles had to stop him. The two fought on the astral plane and Charles won.

Charles soon met another mutant—a man named **Erik Magnus**. Magnus could move metal objects without touching them.

Magnus knew humans feared and hated mutants. He thought the only way for mutants to keep themselves safe was to use their powers to take over the world.

But Charles still dreamed of a world where humans and mutants could live together **peacefully**

Charles and Magnus met and defeated an evil human named **Baron Von Strucker**, who wanted to use his wealth to destroy anyone he didn't like.

Magnus felt that this proved humans were bad. He took the baron's gold and flew away with it, telling Charles he was foolish to believe that mankind was good.

Charles was sad to lose his friend. As he continued his travels, he began to think about returning home.

But during a stop on his journey, Charles encountered an alien named **Lucifer**. He wanted to destroy both humans *and* mutants.

The two fought, and the alien brought down his secret hideaway on top of Charles. Charles survived, but his legs were crushed. **He would never walk again.**

Charles returned home, more determined than ever to find other mutants. He would train them to fight any threat—mutant, human, or alien.

The first mutant Charles found was named **Scott Summers**. Charles called him **Cyclops** for the optic blasts he could shoot from his eyes.

Next, Charles and Cyclops rescued a teenager from an angry mutant-hating mob. The boy, **Bobby Drake**, could turn himself into ice. He called himself **Iceman**.

The growing group found **Warren Worthington III**, who called himself **Angel** for the wings that helped him fly.

Finally, **Hank McCoy** joined the team. Hank was called **The Beast** because of his large hands and feet, which helped him swing like a monkey and punch like a gorilla.

Charles renamed his home **Xavier's School for Gifted Youngsters**. To the outside world, it was just another boarding school. But secretly, it was a school for young mutants to learn how to use their powers for good.

Charles called himself **Professor X** and his team the **X-Men**, because each member had an extraordinary power.

The X-Men soon welcomed their final founding member—**Jean Grey**, called **Marvel Girl**. Jean could move things with her mind.

Professor X built a computer to locate other mutants. He called the machine **Cerebro**. It showed that a mutant was attacking an Army base.

It was the professor's old friend Magnus!

Now known as **Magneto**, he had used the baron's gold to wage war on the human race.

Charles knew that only the X-Men could stop his old friend!

The X-Men arrived at the base just
as Magneto began to attack.

And so the X-Men sprang into action and attacked him right back.

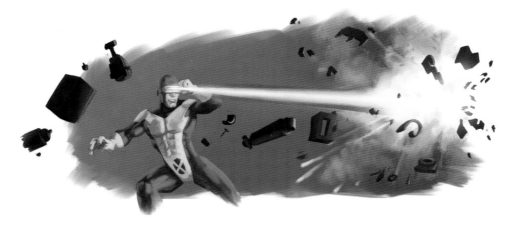

Cyclops tried to blast through Magneto's magnetic field. But he couldn't.

Magneto guided every missile that Marvel Girl tried to send at him right back at her.

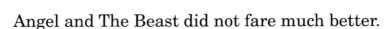

Angel and The Beast did not fare much better.

Magneto attacked them all, but Marvel Girl covered her teammates with a **force field**. The X-Men were not so easily defeated!

The X-Men had come to stop Magneto and turn him over to the police. **But Magneto had escaped.**

The X-Men were disappointed. But Professor X told them he was very proud of them for stopping the attack.

Over the next few months, the X-Men trained in a special gym called the **Danger Room**. The room was filled with obstacles to help the X-Men perfect their abilities.

And Professor X used Cerebro to keep a constant watch for **new mutants**.

He found many! But more often than not, the mutants were evil.

After many battles, the X-Men graduated and became full-fledged heroes. Professor X had never been prouder of his students.

He retired their school uniforms and dressed them in new costumes. But the end of their school day did not mean the end of their missions. In fact, things only got more difficult for the X-Men.

More mutants were appearing each day, and humans were becoming more and more concerned. They were afraid of the mutants' powers. Even though the X-Men tried to protect humans and live Professor Xavier's dream, people treated *all* mutants badly.

As mutants grew in number, so did the X-Men. Cyclops's brother **Alex Summers**—an energy-blasting mutant called **Havok**—and **Lorna Dane**, called **Polaris** for her magnetic abilities, joined the team.

But their group was still too small to fight all of the threats. When the X-Men went missing on a dangerous mission, Professor X had to assemble a **new group** to rescue them.

In Canada, he recruited a mutant named **Wolverine** who could heal himself of any injury and whose claws could cut through almost anything!

In Germany, Charles found **Kurt Wagner**, called **Nightcrawler**, who could move from place to place with just a thought.

Together with Wolverine and Nightcrawler, Professor X decided to seek out more good mutants to help rescue the original X-Men.

In Ireland, Charles found **Sean Cassidy—Banshee**—whose sonic scream could shatter stone and steel.

In Africa, Charles met **Ororo Munroe**, a weather mutant called **Storm**.

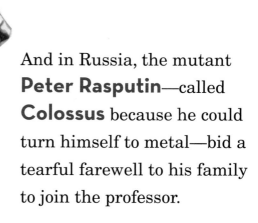

And in Russia, the mutant **Peter Rasputin**—called **Colossus** because he could turn himself to metal—bid a tearful farewell to his family to join the professor.

Charles's new international team wasted no time in their search to find **the Original X-Men**.

The new X-Men rescued the original team from Krakoa, the living island!

The new group decided to stay at Xavier's school. They trained to use their powers. Soon they, too, became X-Men.

They were a kind of family. But no matter what the X-Men did . . .

. . . trouble seemed to find them.

No matter the day, month, or season . . .

Enemies both old and new
were always attacking.

And with every incident, humans became more worried about mutants.

With every battle, **Charles felt the need to fight harder for his dream.**

Whenever Charles felt hope leaving him,

he'd lie down, just as he did when he was a boy,

close his eyes, drift off to sleep . . .

. . . and dream.

Like many great stories,

ours begins with a **troublemaker**.

This one was named **Loki**. He lived in a place called
Asgard with his brother, **Thor**, and their father, **Odin**,
the king of the Realm. All of them had powers you and I
could hardly dream of.

Even though Loki and Thor were both princes, Thor was first in line to be the next king of Asgard. This made Loki very jealous. He thought he should be king.

Loki used his wits to try and get Thor into trouble so he could take his place as king.

But Thor was clever and knew what his brother was up to. As much as he hated to do it, Thor asked Odin's permission to keep Loki prisoner on the **Isle of Silence** so he would stop causing trouble.

Loki was furious. Not only was Thor set to be king, but now Loki could do nothing to stop him.

But Loki had gifts, too. Among them was the power to make people see things that weren't really there. He could also send his spirit places his body could not go.

Loki knew that Thor spent most of his time on Earth, disguised as a doctor named **Don Blake**. And the Earth was filled with **heroes**.

If Loki could find one that the people
of Earth didn't trust—

one who was **strong enough** to win a battle with
someone as powerful as Thor—

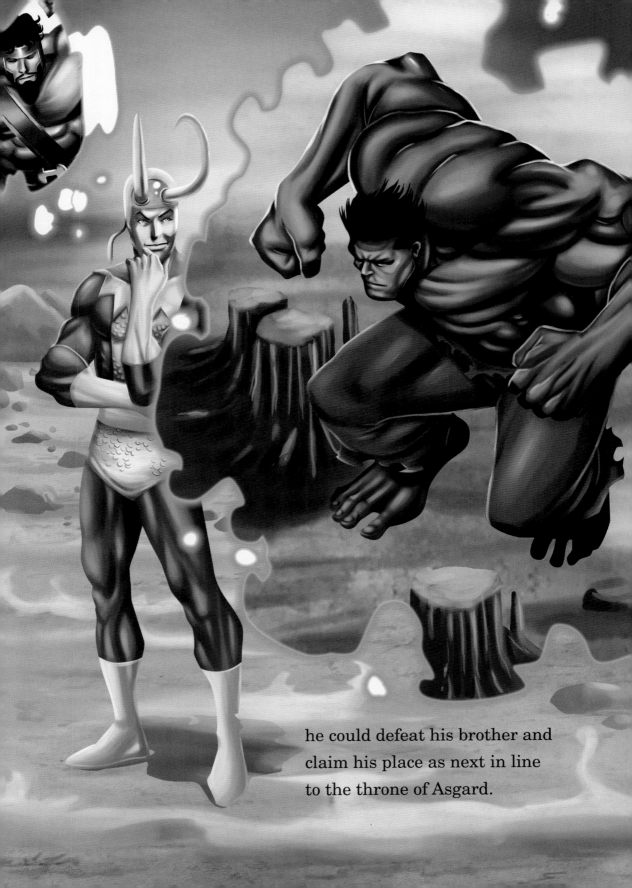

he could defeat his brother and
claim his place as next in line
to the throne of Asgard.

So Loki closed his eyes and sent his spirit to Earth to find the giant green hero, the **Hulk**.

Loki found the Hulk alone, far from any city. He wasted no time putting his plan into action.

He used his powers to make it appear that a nearby
stretch of railway tracks was torn up. Just as Loki
wanted, the Hulk quickly noticed.

He jumped on the tracks to **stop** the train from crashing.

But the people on the train thought the Hulk was trying to hurt them, not help them.

So the Hulk jumped away from the scene.

This is just what Loki had wanted. Thor was sure to try to stop the Hulk. And the Hulk would defeat Thor!

As the news quickly made its way across the country, it caught the attention of **Don Blake**—just as Loki thought it would.

And at nearby Stark Industries Tower, billionaire **Tony Stark**
also heard what the Hulk had been up to. He quickly suited up
as **Iron Man** and rushed to the scene.

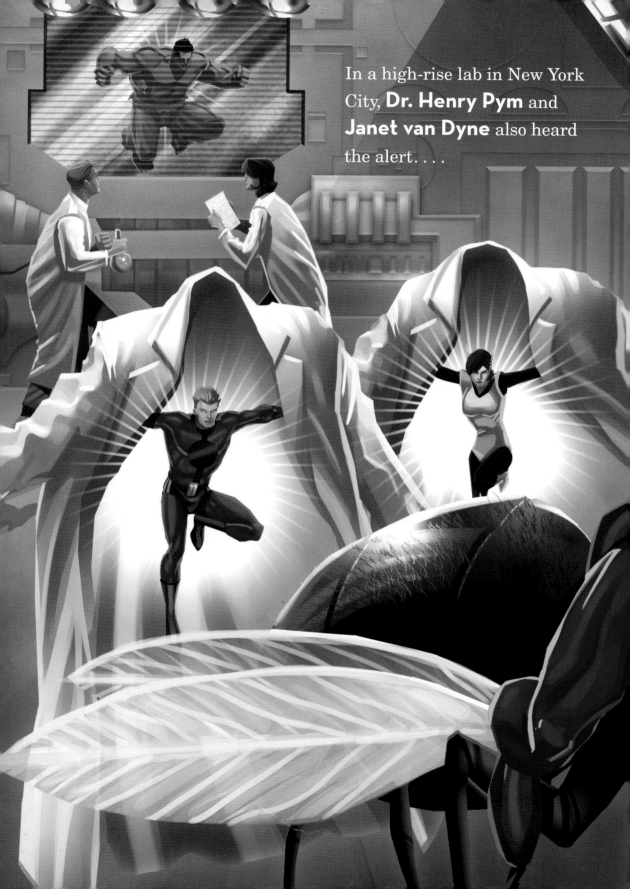

In a high-rise lab in New York City, **Dr. Henry Pym** and **Janet van Dyne** also heard the alert. . . .

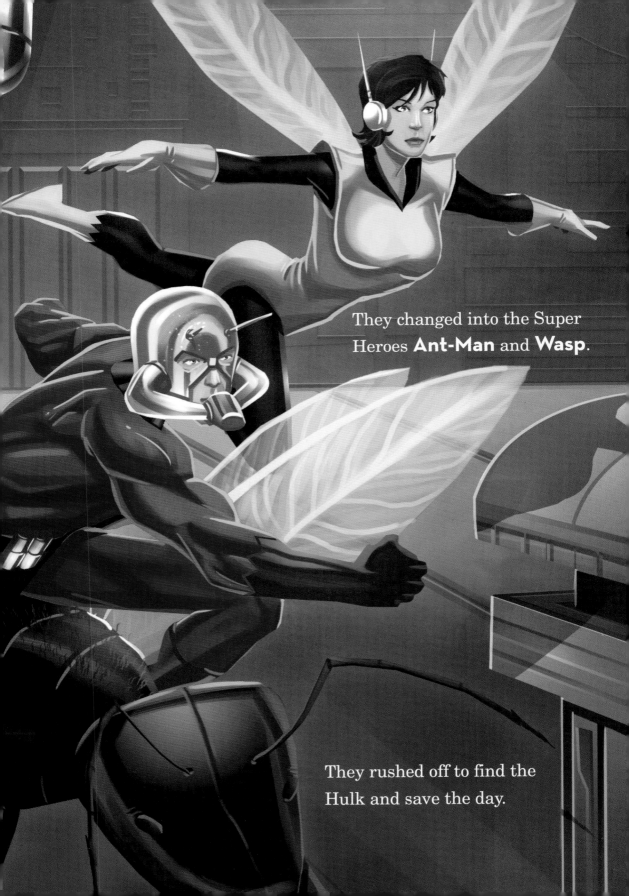

They changed into the Super Heroes **Ant-Man** and **Wasp**.

They rushed off to find the Hulk and save the day.

All the heroes arrived at the same time. The police were happy to see so many of them in one place. Even the Hulk would have trouble stopping **four Super Heroes**.

But someone else wasn't so happy. Loki wanted the Hulk to fight only Thor. He needed to get Thor away from the others.

Loki created an image that only Thor could see.

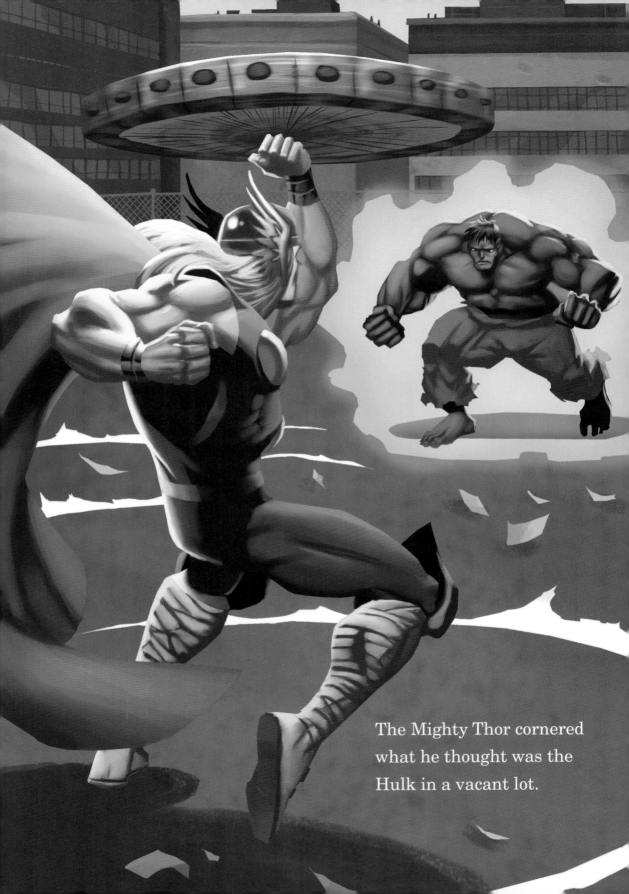

The Mighty Thor cornered what he thought was the Hulk in a vacant lot.

Thor launched his hammer . . .

and that's when he realized his
brother was up to his old tricks.

Only Loki could work magic like this. Thor now knew that the Hulk was not to blame. He flew off toward Asgard to stop Loki and set things right. The others were confused by Thor's leaving. They still thought the Hulk needed to be stopped.

Just then, a **swarm of ants** signaled to Ant-Man
that they had found the **real** Hulk.

Ant-Man told Iron Man and Wasp
to follow them!

The Super Heroes tracked the Hulk to a nearby circus.

The Hulk saw the heroes and quickly disguised himself
as a circus performer.

. . . while Iron Man got the audience to **safety**.

Once Iron Man had cleared the area, he joined the fight.

And as the battle raged on, *another* was about to begin.

Thor raced over the Bifrost
as fast as he could.

He quickly arrived at the Isle of Silence
to bring the real threat to justice!

But Loki had been expecting his brother.

Loki called upon the **Silent Ones**—trolls who lived belowground on the isle.

The Silent Ones attacked Thor and pulled him underground.

But Thor was not
so easily beaten.

Thor defeated the Silent Ones, but in the struggle, **Loki escaped**!

Thor quickly went after his brother.

He found him at the **Bifrost**, which linked Asgard to other realms. Loki had created an illusion to distract Heimdall, the Asgardian who guarded the bridge, and snuck past.

But even though Heimdall hadn't seen the real Loki, Thor had.

Back on Earth, the battle continued.

Thor explained that it was Loki—not the Hulk—
who had caused all the trouble.

But Loki would not give up.

He used his power to make it seem like there were **many** of him.

But one by one,

the heroes figured out which illusions were not the real Loki.

And then one hero discovered the **true villain**.

Loki had been stopped. He would not rule Asgard—today or ever! But it couldn't have been done by any one hero alone. The world would forever remember this as the day a great team was born . . .

. . . and **the Mighty Avengers** first assembled!

Even in a world with scientists as brilliant as Reed Richards, Bruce Banner, and Tony Stark, **Doctor Henry Pym** stood out.

But many scientists found his work too complicated—they couldn't understand what Henry was trying to do. They laughed at his idea of being able to shrink things.

"I'll show them," Henry said to himself. "Then we'll see who's laughing."

Henry worked day and night for months until he had his
formula. Just a few drops of his serum would cause an
object to shrink.

Henry was overjoyed. He'd done what the other scientists
said was impossible. Now there was only one last step:
testing it on a human.

Naturally, Henry tested it on himself.

The serum worked—a little too well. Henry found himself shrinking much faster than he had expected. He looked up in dismay. He had placed the antidote on a window ledge, which was now much too high for him to reach.

Unsure of what to do, Henry stumbled outside. Maybe he could climb up to the window from out there. Unfortunately, Henry wasn't alone.

A **colony of ants** attacked Henry. But the doctor noticed one ant that wasn't attacking. Desperate, Henry jumped on the ant's back. To his surprise, the ant climbed up the wall.

Henry jumped off the ant's back and onto the window ledge. He pushed over the glass beaker holding the serum and climbed in. Immediately, Henry began to grow back to his normal size.

Henry was now fascinated by ants. He learned that ants are extremely strong for their size and can communicate with one another through a combination of sounds and smells. Henry designed a helmet that would enable him to **communicate with ants** and a suit that would shrink as he shrunk.

Henry's research was interrupted by a request from the government. They wanted him to invent a formula that would make people **immune to radiation**.

Before Henry was able to get very far with his formula, however, spies from another country broke into his laboratory. Henry wouldn't tell them anything, so they locked him up and made plans to blow up his lab—with him in it!

Henry was at the mercy of ruthless killers. Or so they thought.

Henry wasn't going to let his lab—or himself—be destroyed.

Henry quickly donned the suit and helmet he'd created. Then he took the shrinking formula.

Ant-Man was born!

Using a rubber band as a slingshot, Henry sent himself
flying through an open window.

Henry landed near the big anthill outside. This time, however,
he wasn't afraid.

Henry had realized that he might be small, but he had all the
strength of a full-grown man.

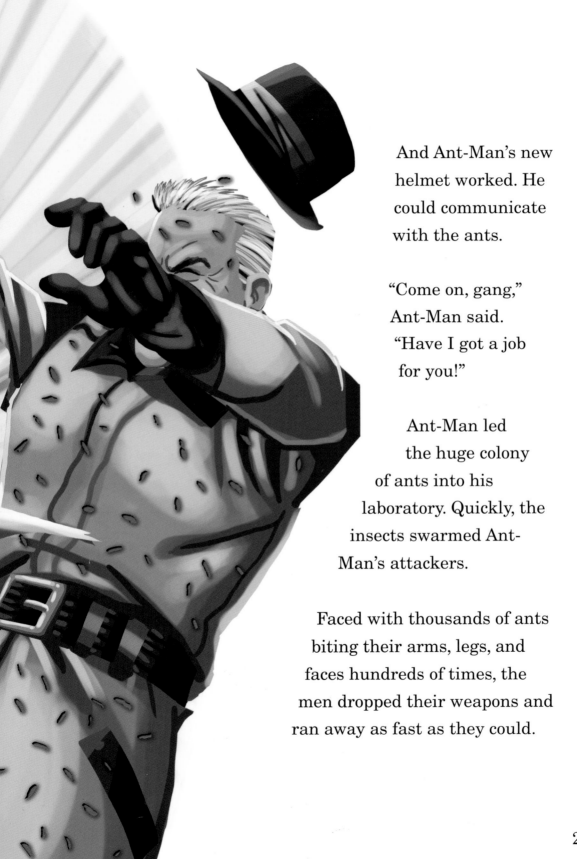

And Ant-Man's new
helmet worked. He
could communicate
with the ants.

"Come on, gang,"
Ant-Man said.
"Have I got a job
for you!"

Ant-Man led
the huge colony
of ants into his
laboratory. Quickly, the
insects swarmed Ant-
Man's attackers.

Faced with thousands of ants
biting their arms, legs, and
faces hundreds of times, the
men dropped their weapons and
ran away as fast as they could.

Henry decided that being a **Super Hero** was a good use of his time. He kept helping people, first as Ant-Man, later as Giant-Man, and soon after as a member of the **Mighty Avengers**.

Many years ago, in the heart of the Canadian wilderness, there lived a savage animal.

The **wolverine**, as it was called, was small, but fierce.

It liked to be alone, but ventured out to hunt
for game when it felt hungry.

It was stout, but quick.

Others lived here, too, on an estate amid the wilderness.

There were three children: **James**, **Rose**, and a boy named "**Dog**."

Dog's father, **Logan**,
lived there, too. He was
the groundskeeper.

The estate belonged to young James's father, **John Howlett**.

James had had a brother. But in those days people did not know as much about science or medicine, and his brother had died.

The estate had felt like something was missing since he'd been gone.

No one felt this emptiness more than James's mother. She rarely left her room, and did little besides think about James's brother.

This left her little time for James.

But for all the sadness in the big place, James had happy times there, too. Mostly with his friends Rose and Dog.

They played together, worked together . . .

. . . grew up together.

But Dog, whose father treated him badly,
became mean as he grew older.

Dog began to dislike James
in the same way the
groundskeeper disliked
James's father.

One night Dog and his father
snuck into the Howlett home.

The two snuck upstairs.

They were angry and jealous
and wanted to fight.

James felt scared, and angry, too.

Suddenly his hands started to feel strange.

He needed to defend his family and his friend Rose.

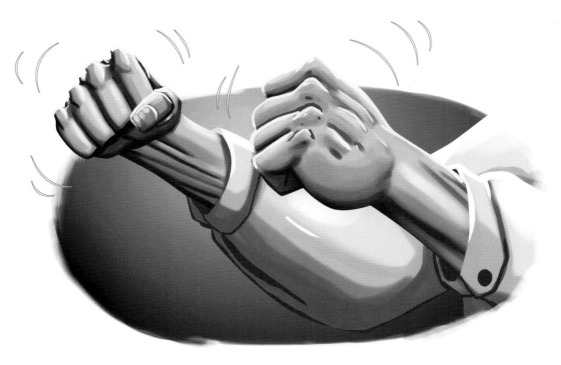

Without warning, James discovered
he was something **more than human**....

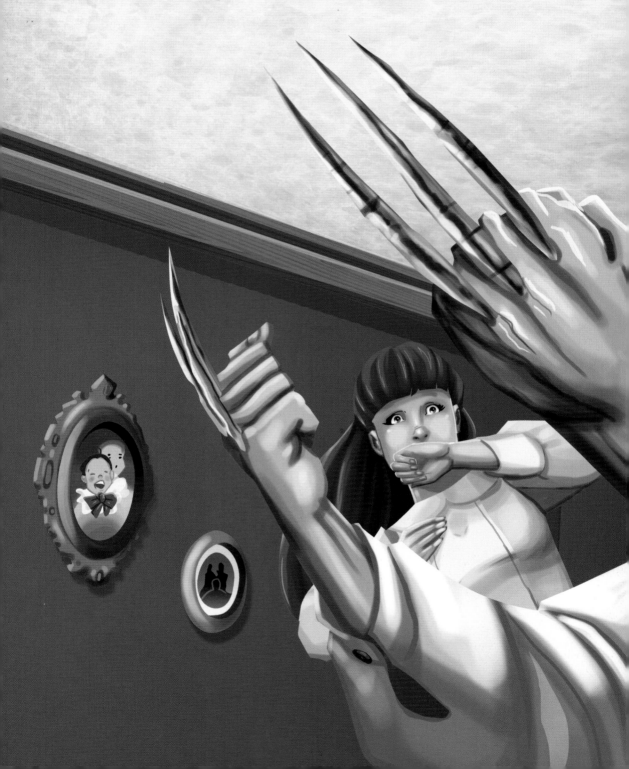

Rose knew people might see James
as something **less**.

She grabbed James by the wrist . . .

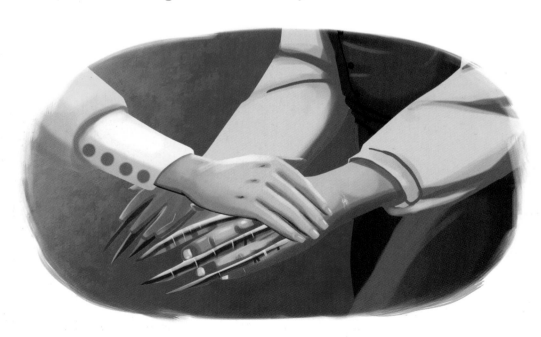

and ran from the house.

James couldn't save his family, but **Rose could save James**.

She took what they needed

and snuck aboard a train.

They needed to go some place no one knew them.

Some place no one would hurt James.

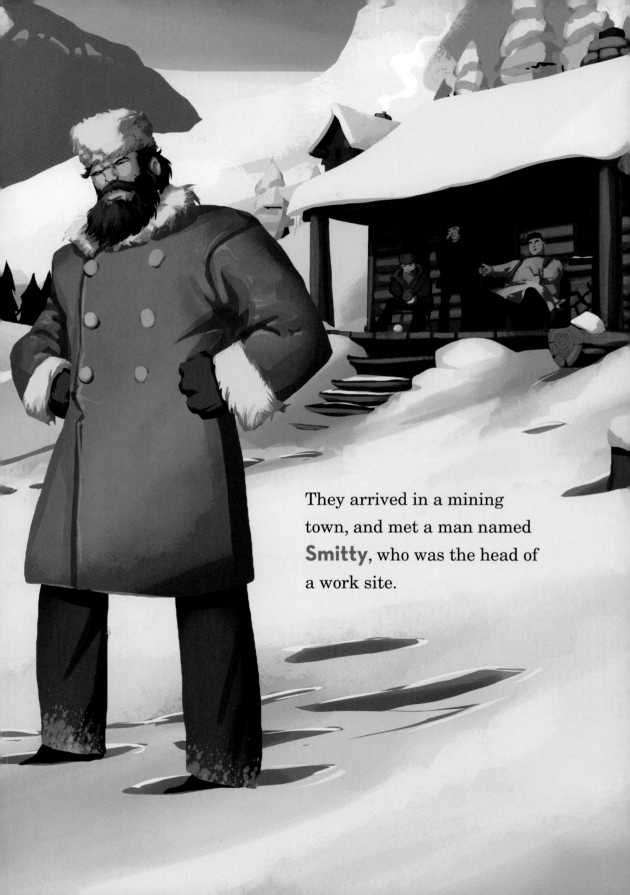

They arrived in a mining town, and met a man named **Smitty**, who was the head of a work site.

Smitty told James to remove his gloves—he wanted to see if his hands were good enough for working.

Rose was scared. She thought Smitty would see James's wounds from his claws, or worse, the claws themselves.

But when James removed his gloves, there were no scars. **James had healed!**

In order to keep their secret safe, Rose told the townspeople that James's name was Logan.

Logan took some hard knocks.
But he always picked himself up.

And as Logan grew up, he left Rose and his old life behind . . .

. . . and learned to control his abilities.

Logan also learned to be strong, stand up for himself and others, and always do what he knew was right.

Logan still had claws and the ability to heal easily, but he
had also learned that he had an animal's senses.

He could see, hear, taste,
smell, and feel as well
as a wild animal.

Logan loved being in the wild. For a time he left behind his life at the camp to live there.

Time continued to pass, but Logan didn't grow much older. His healing ability kept him young. He left the woods, and began to travel the world.

He fought in a great war.

And then he fought in another.

And during peacetime he settled in Japan.

When Logan returned home, he was kidnapped!

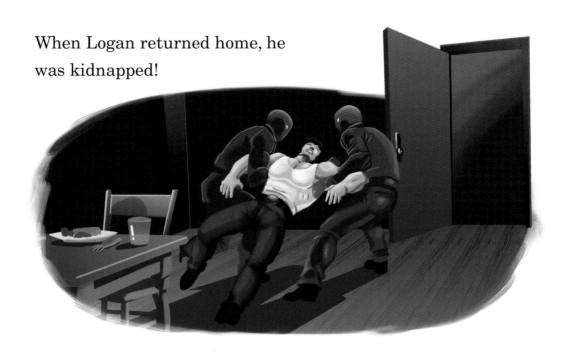

The people who took him knew about his powers. They hooked him up to a machine. They knew that his ability to heal would help him survive their experiment.

Logan's captors erased his memory and coated his bones—and his claws—with an unbreakable metal called **Adamantium**!

Logan managed to escape
into the forest.

He ran . . .

. . . and ran . . .

. . . until he could run no more.

He might have **died**, if he hadn't been found.

James and Heather Hudson found Logan and nursed him back to health. But the only thing he could remember was his name.

James had been working for the government on a Super Hero project called **Department H**. He called himself **Guardian** and Heather called herself **Vindicator**. James thought Logan would make a good hero, too. He gave Logan a costume and a code name . . .

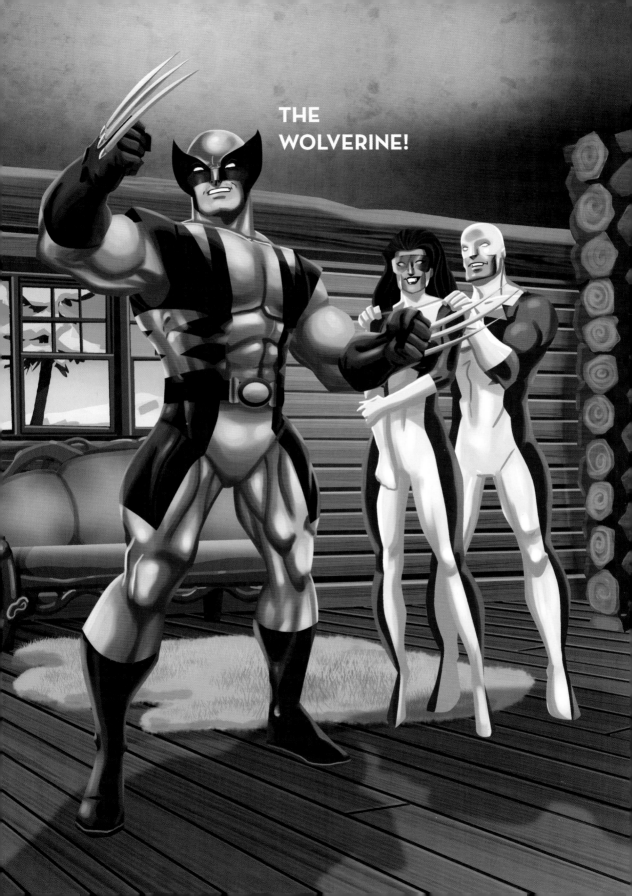

Together Guardian and Wolverine formed a Super Hero
team called **Alpha Flight**.

But often, Wolverine went out
on missions alone.

Even though Wolverine was proud of Alpha Flight and cared deeply for James and Heather, **he didn't feel at home**.

Wolverine left Alpha Flight. He was alone again.

Then, after a lifetime of searching, he eventually found the family he was searching for.

He joined a **team of mutants**. Like him,
they were outcasts. Each was a loner. . . .

But together
they formed the
X-Men.

The Super Hero had been called many things—James, Logan, a Canadian hero, an X-Man. But he knew there was one thing he would always be:

THE UNSTOPPABLE WOLVERINE!

When **Dr. Henry Pym** heard his doorbell ring, he had no idea his entire life was about to change.

"Hello, Dr. Pym," said the older man at the door. "I'm **Dr. Vernon van Dyne**, and this is my daughter, **Janet**."

Dr. van Dyne explained that he was trying to contact other
planets. He hoped Henry's research could help.

"I'm sorry, doctor," Henry said. "I'm afraid I'm too busy, and
my work is just too different."

Dr. van Dyne was disappointed, but being a scientist himself,
he understood.

Dr. van Dyne and Janet returned to his lab, where he continued his experiments. Unfortunately for Dr. van Dyne, he succeeded.

Terribly upset, Janet called the one person she thought
might understand what had happened—Henry Pym.
Henry agreed to send help: Ant-Man. He didn't tell Janet
that *he* secretly was Ant-Man.

Ant-Man took one look at the wrecked lab and knew that Dr. van Dyne's experiment had gone very wrong. His ant friends explained what had really happened.

Ant-Man brought Janet back to his own lab. "It was an alien that did it, wasn't it?" Ant-Man asked. "Which means there's a dangerous alien on the loose. We have to stop it before it hurts others."

Janet looked at Ant-Man. "Can you help me find the alien?"

"I think so," he said. "But I'll need help defeating it."

"I'll do whatever it takes," Janet said.

Ant-Man thought for a moment. Then he took off his helmet.

"Henry Pym?" Janet gasped. Then she nodded. "Your secret is safe with me," she said, staring into his eyes. "What can I do to help? I'll do anything."

Henry injected Janet with the secret formula he invented.

"This will enable you to shrink down to the size of a wasp," he explained. "And you'll be able to grow wings and antennae."

"I assume," Janet said, "that you've got a costume that will shrink along with me?"

She had become **Wasp**.

"Oh!" Janet gasped as she tried shrinking for the first time. "I feel so strange!"

"You get used to it," Ant-Man said.

"What are we waiting for?" said Wasp. "Let's go!"

Ant-Man's ant friends had located the alien. But even without their help, the alien wouldn't have been hard to find.

"It's the size of a building!" Wasp said.

"And look how powerful it is!" Ant-Man agreed. "What are we going to do?"

"This!" Wasp said. She flew right at the monster. But her attack didn't work—she merely bounced off it.

"Wasp!" Ant-Man yelled, rushing toward her. "Are you okay?"

"I'm fine," Wasp replied. "Just a bit bruised. That thing seems unstoppable. And what's this stuff all over me?"

"That's odd," Ant-Man said. "It's some kind of acid on your costume where you touched the alien."

"Is the alien made of acid?" Wasp asked. "And could you make an antidote to it?"

Ant-Man and Wasp raced back to the lab. Soon, an antidote was ready.

"You *are* one of the world's greatest scientists," Wasp said.

Henry blushed. "Now we need to find a way to get enough of this stuff on the alien."

"I think I know how," said Wasp. "We'll just need to borrow some equipment from the Army."

The Army was
more than happy
to lend Ant-Man
and Wasp a tank.

"Here's hoping,"
Ant-Man said.

"Have a little faith,"
said Wasp.

She was right. Their
solution worked
perfectly. As soon as
the alien was hit by
the antidote, it began
to fade away.

"Nice work," Wasp said to Ant-Man.

"I couldn't possibly have done it without you," Ant-Man replied. "We make a good team. How do you feel about continuing this partnership?"

The Wasp grinned. "I feel pretty good about it."

And that is how Ant-Man and Wasp became partners.

There is a place where the earth is frozen and the water is ice. The shoreline is like a wall between two worlds—the sea and the land.

Both are silent and still.

And empty.

But this was not always so.

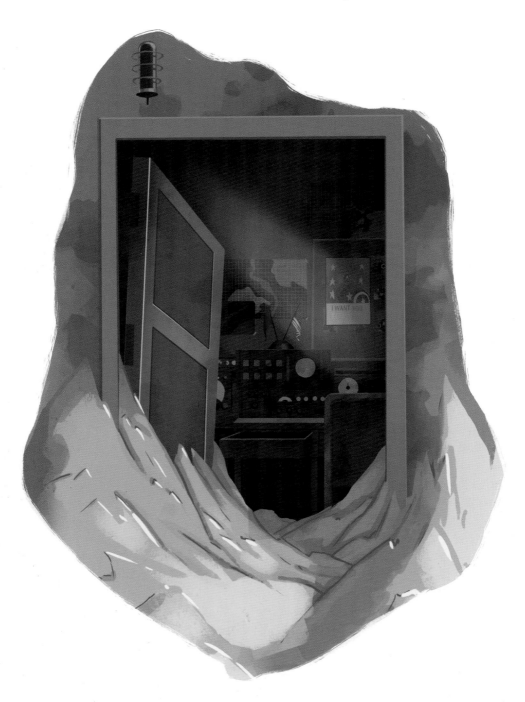

Long ago, soldiers stood watch here.

They fought in terrible wars,
but they did not fight alone.

They fought in an age
of another kind of hero.

Among these heroes were **Captain America**—Super-Soldier and defender of freedom—and **Namor**, prince of the undersea kingdom Atlantis.

One day, without warning, the heroes
suddenly disappeared.

Captain America had plunged into
the icy ocean while trying to stop
a dangerous plane from taking off.

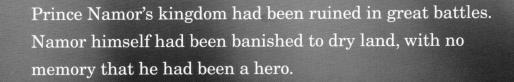

Prince Namor's kingdom had been ruined in great battles. Namor himself had been banished to dry land, with no memory that he had been a hero.

Weeks passed, then years, then decades . . .

The world became used to a world without Super Heroes. Until . . .

. . . the Super Heroes returned!

The new heroes
possessed incredible
and amazing powers!

Thor could summon all the might of thunder.

Tony Stark wore powerful armor to become Iron Man.

Ant-Man and **Wasp** could become bigger or smaller.

Together, they formed a team of Super Heroes called the **Mighty Avengers**!

The Avengers were searching for their friend **the Incredible Hulk**, who had gone missing after the team's last battle.

They also wanted to investigate a rumor they had heard; after all these long years, **Namor had returned**.

But none of them were prepared for what they saw next. . . .

The Hulk was with Namor, who had indeed returned.
But the Atlantean seemed very angry—not at all like
the hero they had heard tales of.

The heroes knew that Namor's powers came from the water, and in a place like this, with lots of it nearby, he would be hard to beat.

Having the Hulk on his side made it even harder.

Namor told the Avengers that his kingdom, Atlantis, was in ruins. He thought humans had destroyed it. To get revenge, he planned to defeat **Earth's Mightiest Heroes**! Then he would rule over the human race!

The Avengers couldn't figure out why
the Hulk was fighting alongside Namor.

He was their friend. He was a hero.

Just when the battle seemed lost and
the last Avenger was about to fall—

It had all been part of the Hulk's plan: he would make Namor think he was on his side, but in the end he would help the Avengers win the battle.

The Avengers couldn't let Namor escape. They jumped
in their Quinjet and rushed into the water to go after
the Sub-Mariner. But as soon as they were beneath
the surface, Iron Man noticed something.

It was a man frozen in a block of ice.

Ant-Man swam out of the craft and grabbed him.

Ant-Man brought the frozen figure back to the Quinjet and placed him in the sick bay. Iron Man carefully warmed the ice with his repulsor rays to free the man.

The Avengers couldn't believe what they were seeing.
They knew this man from history books.
He was Captain America!

Captain America had no idea the Avengers were friendly. But
Iron Man made it clear when he handed him his shield . . .

. . . and welcomed Captain America back to the world.

Iron Man explained that **many years had passed** since the world had last seen Cap. The ice must have kept him in a kind of sleep where he didn't age.

Iron Man brought Captain America to a place in the craft where he could have some time to himself.

Everything Captain America found there was new to him.

He had no idea how to use any of the things the Avengers had on their ship.

NEWS **4** HAS THE SEA KING RETURNED?

...ARK INDUSTRIES POSTS GAINS · RICHARDS CONFIRMS SH... ...SIGLAIN P...

He finally figured out how to turn on the TV. There, he saw a man who looked familiar. Captain America thought he might have known him long ago, but he couldn't remember.

But before Captain America could wonder more about the man on the screen, **something rocked the craft**!

Namor had returned, and he had brought **all the armies of Atlantis** with him!

The Avengers rushed onto land, where they knew
the Atlanteans would be weaker.

The Atlantean armies quickly followed.

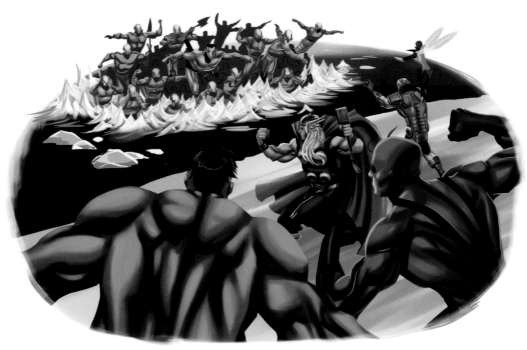

Thor raised his hammer and cried out for the battle to begin.

The Avengers fought bravely . . .

. . . but the Super Heroes were soon outnumbered.

Just then, someone who was not
an Avenger stepped in.

The tide began to turn.

After a long battle, the Avengers—together with
Captain America—drove off Namor and his army.
They had stopped him from waging war on the world!

Neither Cap nor the team could have done it alone.

It was decided to do the only thing that made sense. . . .

The Courageous Captain America agreed to become
the newest member of the Mighty Avengers!

The X-Men were a special kind of Super Hero team. They were **mutants**—heroes born with special abilities. **Professor X**, himself a mutant, led the X-Men in an ongoing fight to keep the world safe from evil mutants. Professor X used his special computer, **Cerebro**, to locate a mutant that was more powerful than any he had seen before.

He told the X-Men to board their plane, the Blackbird, and
find the mutant in case it was evil and needed to be stopped!

The flight was quick in the superfast jet. Once they landed, the X-Men left the plane one by one: **Cyclops**, who shot beams from his eyes, and his brother, **Havok**, who could shoot them from his body. **Marvel Girl** could move things with her mind. **Iceman** was able to turn himself into frozen water. Angel's wings helped him fly. **Polaris** could move metal like a magnet. And **Beast** was, well, a beast!

Before the X-Men had even started looking for the mutant, something terrible sneaked up behind them.

"Behind us, look! It's . . . it's . . ." warned Polaris.

"Quick, everybody scatter! Get moving before we . . ." Havok cried.

Only Cyclops hadn't seen what was creeping up from behind. And before he had a chance to act, the other X-Men were gone, and he had blacked out!

The next thing Cyclops knew, he was back on the Blackbird. His costume was torn and he felt weak. Then he noticed something: his special visor that kept his rays in check was gone. But then he realized something even worse.

"My eyes!" he cried, "They're normal. . . powerless!"

Then he noticed one more thing: the plane was flying on autopilot. Blackbird was heading back to the X-Men's mansion in New York. And Cyclops couldn't stop it!

Professor X was shocked when the plane landed and Cyclops rushed into the mansion.

"Cyclops, what happened? Where are the others?" he asked.

Cyclops told the professor everything he knew. But before Cyclops had finished his story, his eyes started to glow bright red.

The professor had never before seen the X-Men so
thoroughly defeated. Other than Cyclops, he was not
sure that anyone on the team was even still alive.

The X-Men were his students, his friends; they had
become like his family.

Professor X knew what he needed to do.

The Professor sat at Cerebro and searched the entire globe for mutants. The only way he would be able to save the X-Men would be to gather together a new group of X-Men. They would be the original team's only hope.

In Germany, Professor X saved Kurt Wagner, called **Nightcrawler**, from an angry mob.

"I can help you find your true potential," Professor X told him. And in Canada, Professor X made the hero called **Wolverine** an offer he couldn't refuse.

"I'm giving you a chance to be a free agent," he told Wolverine.

In Ireland, he found **Banshee**, who had a powerful sonic scream. In Arizona, he convinced an Apache named John Proudstar, called **Thunderbird**, whose strength was unmatched, to join him. In Japan, he called in the mutant **Sunfire**.

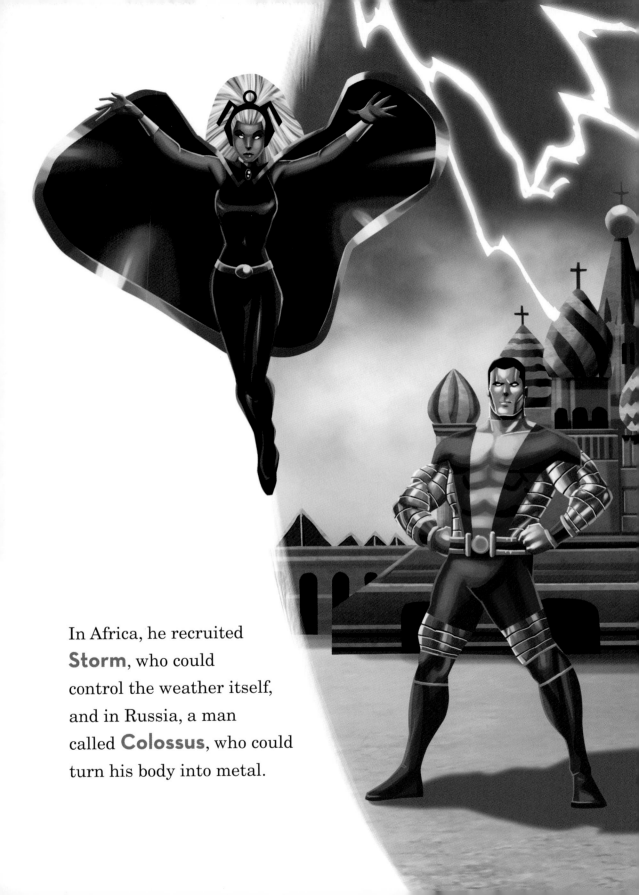

In Africa, he recruited
Storm, who could
control the weather itself,
and in Russia, a man
called **Colossus**, who could
turn his body into metal.

Once the team was complete, Professor X introduced the new X-Men to Cyclops.

"You have been called here because the X-Men have disappeared," Cyclops told them. "You seven are our only hope. We need to go back to the island of Krakoa, where they vanished. Then we need to find the original X-Men and the mutant that took them!"

Before long the new X-Men were on Krakoa. As they
searched the island, they came across an old temple.
Could the mutant they were looking for be based there?
The new X-Men didn't waste any time finding out!

When they broke down the temple wall, they found part of what they were looking for. The original X-Men were inside, held captive by strange-looking tubes.

"The mutant wanted you to come and bring others with you," Angel said. "It feeds on other mutants' energies. It was all a trap! And worst of all, we came to this island *looking* for a mutant. . . . But the mutant is the island itself!"

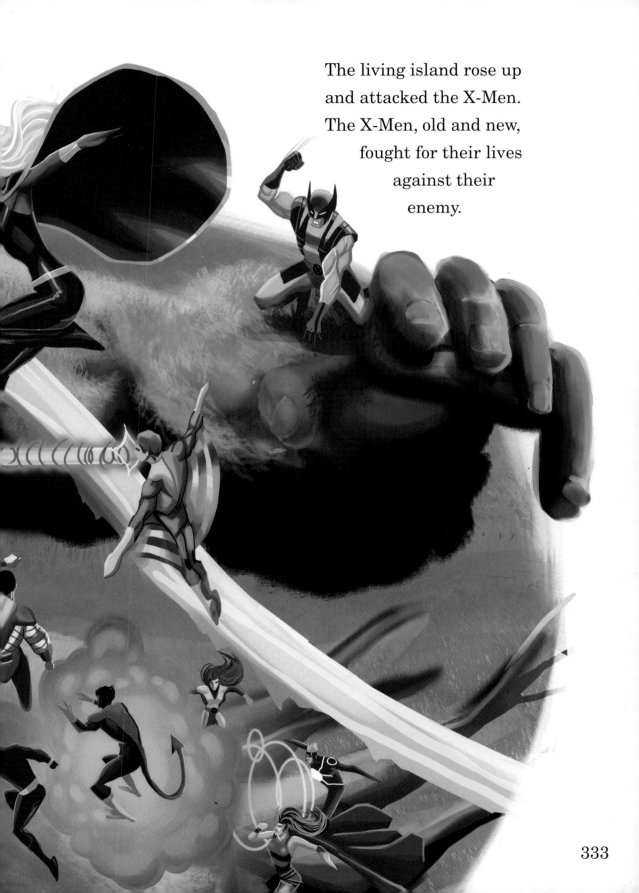

The living island rose up and attacked the X-Men. The X-Men, old and new, fought for their lives against their enemy.

Eventually, using their combined powers, they
defeated the creature.

Iceman created an ice boat to keep the team afloat,
and the sheer force of the X-Men's combined
powers sent the island of Krakoa
into outer space.

And from that battle a young group of mutant heroes was born—**an all-new, all-different team of X-Men!**

Reed **Richards** loved science. It was his passion. He always won first place in the science fair at school, and at home he'd rather study mathematical formulas than play with other kids. He found the world of science and math fascinating. There was so much to learn, and Reed wanted to know everything.

Reed was rewarded for his knowledge of science. He even
got to go to the state science fair. His teachers were proud
of him. The more Reed learned, the more he realized just
how much there was to learn. He was always reading
about new scientific discoveries
and dreaming that one
day he would be a
world-famous scientist.

Reed didn't lose his love for science as he grew older. He kept studying and loved it more than ever. By the time he was a teenager and most of his friends were starting high school, Reed was sought after by all of the country's best colleges and universities.

Reed studied so much that he didn't have time for friends.
When he found out that he was going to have a college
roommate, he was very nervous. Not only was he awkward
at making new friends, he had never had a roommate before.
He wasn't sure how to act. His heart pounded as he opened
the door to his new dorm room.

When Reed opened the door, he saw a big guy who didn't seem very friendly.

"Hi, I'm Reed," he said, extending his hand.

Ben took it and smiled. "You must be the youngest kid on campus."

"Possibly," Reed said nervously.

"Well, I might be the biggest," Ben said with a laugh.

Reed realized that Ben wasn't what he appeared to be. He was a nice guy.

Reed and Ben became fast friends. They helped each other in class. In the evenings and on weekends, they ate meals together at the local diner. Reed loved cheering Ben on during his wrestling matches. They were always together. Reed learned how to be a good friend, and he enjoyed it.

One day Reed showed Ben something that he'd never
shown anyone else.

They were Reed's plans for a new type of spacecraft. He
had been working on it for years. This rocket wouldn't
need fuel. It would use cosmic energy, like the sun's rays,
to power itself. It wouldn't use up the Earth's air, water, or
land. And best of all, it could be used over and over again!

"Wow, you have some fun ideas," Ben said as he looked at the diagram of the ship.

Reed really believed that he could make the ship. "I'm going to do it, Ben."

"Well, if you do, I'll pilot it."

After graduation, the two roommates parted ways.

Even though he had been joking with Reed about piloting the spaceship, Ben joined the Marines. And there he learned to fly planes and spacecraft.

Although they didn't live together anymore, the two friends kept in touch.

Reed continued his studies, all the while focusing on his perfect spaceship. He moved out of the dorm and into an apartment downtown.

Without Ben around, Reed was lonely. He became close friends with his landlord's niece, **Sue Storm**, and her younger brother, **Johnny**.

When Reed got the fantastic news that the government was going to help pay for his spacecraft project, he told Sue and Johnny even before he told Ben.

Reed spent the next few years building his ship. His friends were very proud of him.

But before they could celebrate, the group was given some bad news. The government thought Reed's project had become too expensive, with no proof it would work. It was to be shut down immediately.

Reed made a decision. He was going to test his ship before it could be destroyed.

Ben told Reed he couldn't do this without a pilot.

The ship worked! The flight into space was smooth and quick. But suddenly, the cabin went dark. Johnny felt very hot. Ben felt so heavy, he couldn't move. Reed's head felt as if it would burst. And Sue felt sleepier than she ever had in her life.

The ship rocketed to a rough but safe landing back on Earth. The crew escaped, and Reed figured that the ship must have been hit by a cosmic storm.

Suddenly, Sue seemed to disappear! She'd become invisible! But as quickly as it had happened, she reappeared. She called herself the **Invisible Woman**.

Something had happened to Ben, too. Sue yelled out and called him a "**thing**"! It was the only way to describe what he'd become.

Reed had also changed. It seemed his body could bend into any shape imaginable. He called himself **Mr. Fantastic**.

Johnny could now set his whole body on fire. He called himself the **Human Torch**.

The group realized that Reed's experiment may not have worked the way he had wanted it to, but it had done something else incredible: it had given them fantastic powers. And they needed to use those powers to help mankind, just as Reed had intended to do with his spacecraft.

And from that moment on, the group of friends would be known as the amazing, incredible, awesome **Fantastic Four**!

Daredevil. The man without fear. He may not be afraid of anything—but every criminal in New York City is terrified of him.

What these criminals don't know is that Daredevil is really just plain old **Matt Murdock**.

And although it's hard to believe, the daring acrobat who leaps from building to building high above the city streets . . . is blind!

Young Matt Murdock would have given just about anything to play ball like the other kids. But he couldn't.

"No games for you, Matt," his father said. "And never any fights. Promise me you'll be the best student in school."

The other kids teased him. "There goes the daredevil himself," they would call. But Matt kept his promise.

One day, Matt saw an old man about to get hit by a truck. Without stopping to think about it, Matt ran into the street and pushed the old man to safety.

But Matt himself got hit. The truck was loaded with barrels of **toxic waste**. This poisonous substance splashed all over Matt, coating him from head to toe.

When Matt woke up in the hospital, he found that he had lost the use of his eyes. **He was blind.**

But Matt found something else: all his other senses were much more powerful than before. He could hear people talking from blocks away. He could tell who people were by the smell of their perfume or shaving cream. He could read books just by feeling the ink.

But things weren't going so well for Matt's dad. He was a boxer. But he was getting too old—no one would let him fight anymore. Finally, in desperation, Matt's dad agreed to work with a man called **the Fixer**.

Then one day Matt's father refused to do what the Fixer asked of him.

"Make sure 'Battlin' Jack' Murdock never fights again," the Fixer told his goons.

And he never did.

Matt felt that losing his father was even worse than losing his sight.

He decided he would honor his father by keeping his promise: Matt went to law school. Once again, he was the best in his class. And he never fought.

After law school, Matt and his roommate, **Foggy Nelson**, opened up a law firm together.

Matt couldn't stop thinking about his dad. He had promised his father he would never fight.

"Wait!" he said to himself. "*Matt* promised. But . . . what if it wasn't Matt Murdock doing the fighting? What if I became . . . 'Daredevil'?"

Daredevil's amazing senses enabled him to do just about anything.

And his senses combined to give him a sort of radar. Daredevil could leap off a building and know exactly how far away the nearest ledge, flagpole, or telephone wire was.

Daredevil decided he was ready to face his father's killer.

He decided the Fixer was going to get a surprise visit from a certain Super Hero.

When Daredevil entered the gym, everyone stopped and stared.

"Having trouble believing your eyes?" Daredevil asked. "Believe me, I know how that feels. I'm looking for the Fixer—I'm not concerned with the rest of you."

Daredevil found the Fixer and chased him down into the subway.

"Who are you?" the Fixer gasped. "What do you want?"

"'Battlin' Jack' Murdock," Daredevil said. "Admit you were responsible for his fate!"

"Sure, I admit it. So what?" the Fixer laughed.

Standing behind the Fixer was a cop.
He had heard the whole confession!

"What now?" Daredevil wondered. He'd done what he'd set
out to do: he had gotten justice for his father.

"But there's a city full of people out there," he reasoned. "And
a lot of them are in situations like mine. They need someone
to help."

Daredevil grinned. "And whenever someone needs help,
Daredevil will be there!"